# French

## Key Stage 1
## For ages 5-7

## Practise & Learn

Published by CGP

Editors:
Heather Gregson
Lucy Loveluck
Matteo Orsini Jones
Holly Poynton

With thanks to Florence Bonneau, Sandrine Moyle
and Jennifer Underwood for the proofreading.

ISBN: 978 1 84762 985 2

With thanks to Jan Greenway for the copyright research.

Groovy website: www.cgpbooks.co.uk
Printed by Elanders Ltd, Newcastle upon Tyne
Jolly bits of clipart from CorelDRAW®

Based on the classic CGP style created by Richard Parsons.

# Contents

Hello!     4
Bonjour!

How are you?     6
Ça va?

What is your name?     8
Comment t'appelles-tu?

Numbers     10
Les nombres

Colours     12
Les couleurs

My family     14
Ma famille

Animals     16
Les animaux

Clothes     18
Les vêtements

What do you like doing?     20
Qu'est-ce que tu aimes faire?

Food     22
La nourriture

In my pencil case     24
Dans ma trousse

Where do you live?     26
Où habites-tu?

My house     28
Chez moi

Do you remember?     30
Tu te rappelles?

# Hello!
## Bonjour!

This is how you say hello and goodbye in French.

**Bonjour!**
Hello!

**Au revoir!**
Goodbye!

**Bonjour!**
Hello!

**Au revoir!**
Goodbye!

Draw a red circle around the characters saying "hello".
Draw a green circle around the ones saying "goodbye".

Bonjour!

Au revoir!

Au revoir!

Bonjour!

Draw lines through these letters to spell "au revoir".

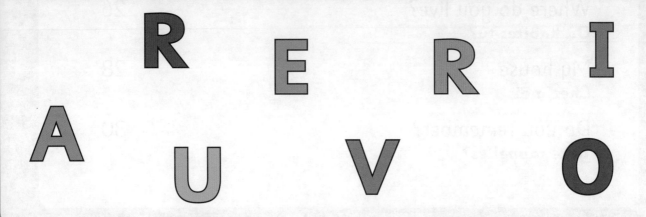

R E R I
A U V O

Colour in the letters to spell out "bonjour".

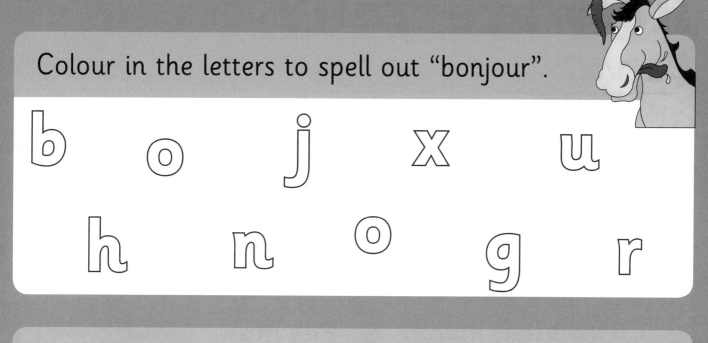

Complete the sentences below in English.

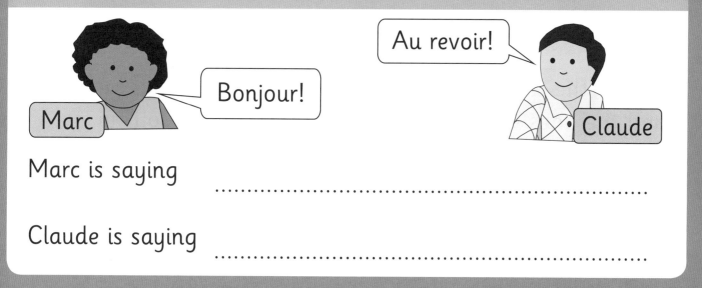

Marc is saying ........................................................................

Claude is saying ........................................................................

Fill in the missing letters in the speech bubbles.

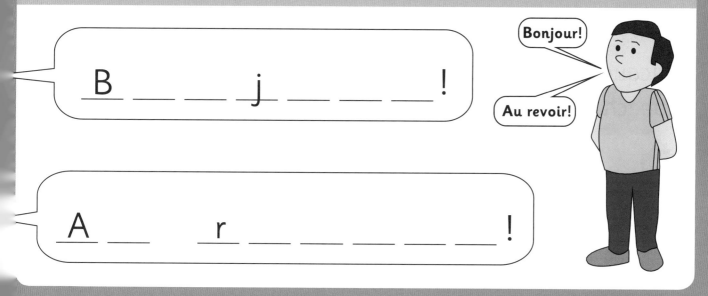

B _ _ _ j _ _ _ _ !

A _ _ r _ _ _ _ _ _ !

# How are you?
## Ça va?

To ask "How are you?" in French, you say: **"Ça va?"**

> **Ça va?** How are you?

To answer you could say:

> **Ça va bien, merci.**
> I'm fine, thank you.

> **Pas mal.**
> Not bad.

Colour the teddies who are asking "How are you?" in blue, and the ones who are saying "I'm fine, thank you" in pink.

Jacques has asked Lily how she is. Complete Lily's speech bubble so that she says "not bad" in French.

P _ _ _ _ _ _ L .

Éric is all confused. Rewrite his answer below with the words in the correct order.

Ça va?

Éric

Antoine

Bien va merci ça.

..............................

..............................

Colour in the letters which spell out "ça va?".

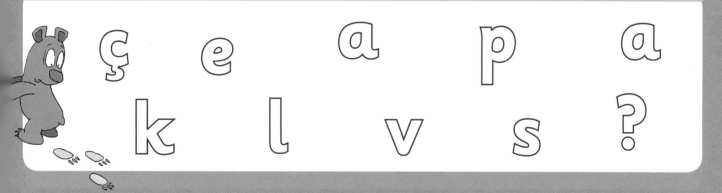

ç e a p a

k l v s ?

Fill in the blanks to finish the conversation.

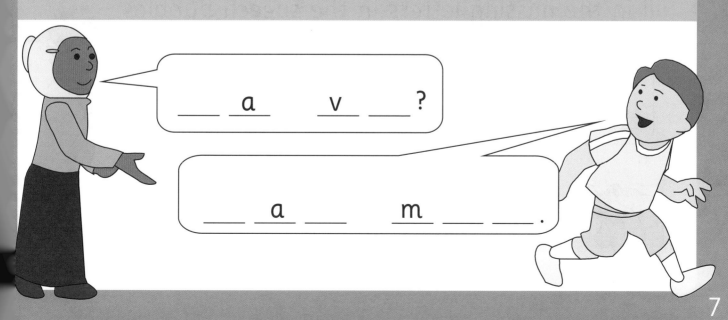

__ a __ v __ ?

__ __ a __ m __ __ .

# What is your name?
## Comment t'appelles-tu?

To ask "What is your name?" in French, you say

**Comment t'appelles-tu?**

To say "My name is..." in French, you say

**Je m'appelle...**

---

Draw lines through the boxes to make two sentences.

appelles

Je

-tu?

m'

Comment — t'

Paul.

appelle

---

Fill in the missing letters in the speech bubbles.

C _ m _ _ _ n _
t ' _ p _ _ _ _ _ e - _ u ?

J _ _ _ ' _ p _ _ _ _ e
A b b y .

Circle the correct French words to match the English.

**Hello**
Comment t'appelles-tu?

Ça va?

Bonjour

**How are you?**
Je m'appelle

Au revoir

Ça va?

**My name is**
Au revoir

Je m'appelle

Comment t'appelles-tu?

Gerald has sent you a secret message in French. Follow the instructions to find out what it says.

| C | a | o | m | m | l | e | b | n | u | t |
|---|---|---|---|---|---|---|---|---|---|---|

t' | a | p | p | h | e | l | u | l | e | s | - | w | t | u | ?

Cross out the blue boxes and write down what's left.

............................................................................

............................................................................

Write down what this means in English.

............................................................................

............................................................................

9

# Numbers
## Les nombres

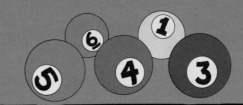

Here are the numbers from one to ten in French.

1 un
2 deux
3 trois
4 quatre
5 cinq
6 six
7 sept
8 huit
9 neuf
10 dix

Write the French word for each number below.

7 | sept
1 |

3 |
4 |

8 |
6 |

Draw lines to match the numbers to the French words.

10    quatre    5    neuf    2

cinq    9    deux    4    dix

Count how many items there are in each group.
Write the number in French in the box.

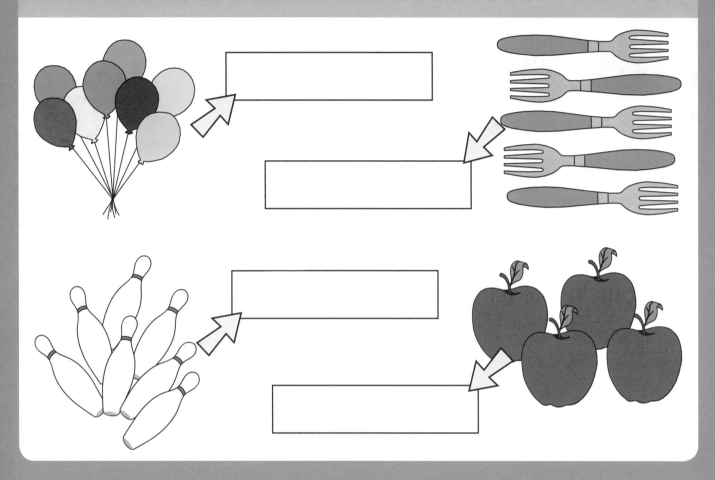

Draw the correct number of fish in each fish bowl.

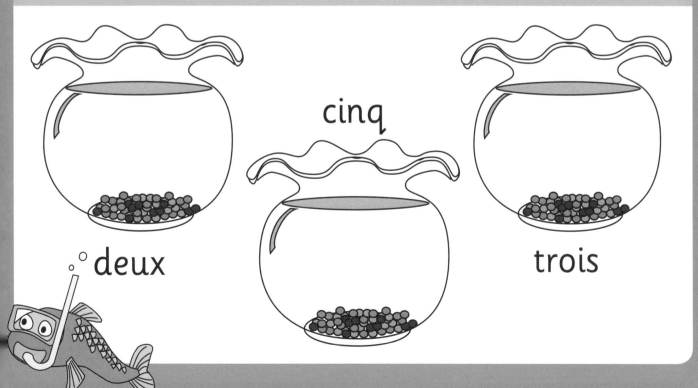

cinq

deux

trois

# Colours
## Les couleurs

rouge

vert

blanc

bleu

jaune

noir

Colour in the icing below using the correct colour.

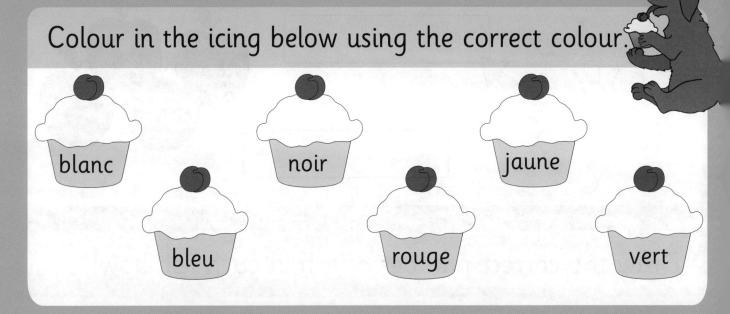

blanc

noir

jaune

bleu

rouge

vert

Write the English words next to the French words.

vert _____

rouge _____

noir _____

bleu _____

blanc _____

jaune _____

## Draw lines to match the balloons to the right colours.

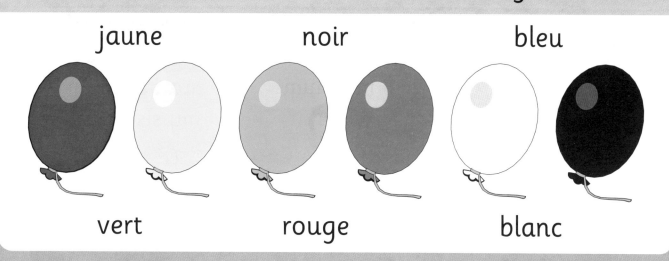

jaune     noir     bleu

vert     rouge     blanc

## Find the French words for colours in the word search.

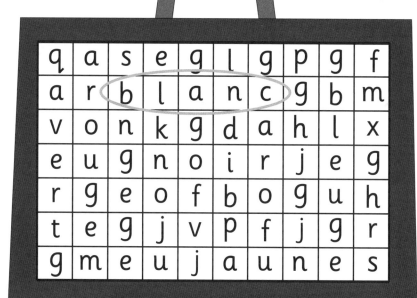

| q | a | s | e | g | l | g | p | g | f |
|---|---|---|---|---|---|---|---|---|---|
| a | r | b | l | a | n | c | g | b | m |
| v | o | n | k | g | d | a | h | l | x |
| e | u | g | n | o | i | r | j | e | g |
| r | g | e | o | f | b | o | g | u | h |
| t | e | g | j | v | p | f | j | g | r |
| g | m | e | u | j | a | u | n | e | s |

blanc
noir
bleu
vert
jaune
rouge

## Label the items with the correct colour in French.

13

# My family
## Ma famille

For each picture, colour in the family member that's mentioned.

**Remember!**
The word for "my" changes. If you are talking about a boy, use "**mon**", if you are talking about a girl use "**ma**".

Look at the picture on the opposite page. Draw a circle around the picture of the correct family member.

mon frère

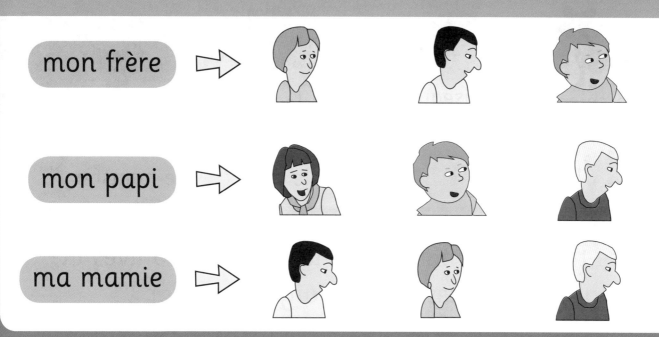

mon papi

ma mamie

Unscramble the letters to make the names of family members.

m p a
a o p n

.......... mon ..........................

m a i e
a m m

n m m a
a a m

.......... ..........................

e m o
è r n r f

.......... ..........................

15

# Animals
## Les animaux

le chien   l'oiseau   le lapin   le cheval

le poisson   le chat   le hamster

Write the French name for the animal who lives in each of these places. Don't forget **le**, **la** or **l'**.

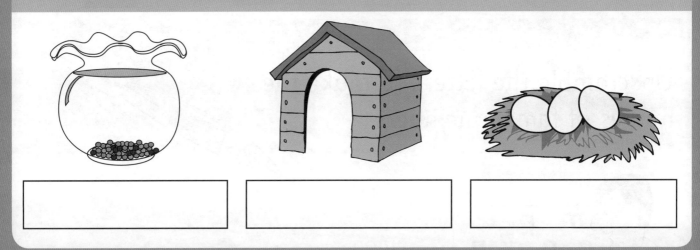

Draw a picture in each frame for each word below.

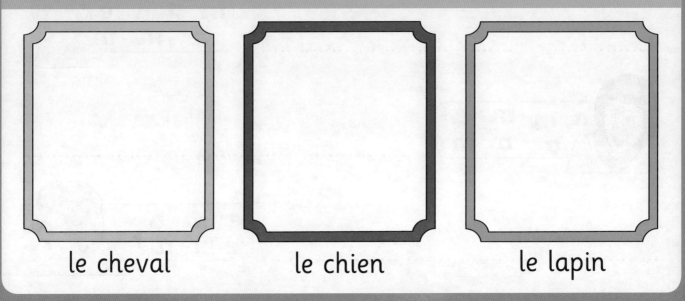

le cheval   le chien   le lapin

# Practise and Learn

# French

# Ages 5-7

# Answers

This section shows each of the pages from the book with the answers filled out.

The pages are laid out in the same way as the book itself, so the questions can be easily marked by you, or by your child.

There are also helpful learning tips with some of the pages.

**4**

## Hello!
### Bonjour!

This is how you say hello and goodbye in French.

Bonjour!
Hello!

Bonjour!
Hello!

Au revoir!
Goodbye!

Au revoir!
Goodbye!

Draw a red circle around the characters saying "hello".
Draw a green circle around the ones saying "goodbye".

Bonjour! — red
green
Au revoir!
Au revoir!
Bonjour! — red
green

Draw lines through these letters to spell "au revoir".

A R E R I
U V O

**5**

Colour in the letters to spell out "bonjour".

b o j x u
h n o g r

Complete the sentences below in English.

Au revoir!

Bonjour!

Marc

Claude

Marc is saying ____hello____

Claude is saying ____goodbye____

Fill in the missing letters in the speech bubbles.

Bonjour!

Au revoir!

_B o n j o u r_ !

_A u   r e v o i r_ !

4

5

## 6 How are you?
### Ça va?

To ask "How are you?" in French, you say: "**Ça va?**"

**Ça va?**    How are you?

To answer you could say:

**Ça va bien, merci.**
I'm fine, thank you.

**Pas mal.**
Not bad.

Ça va?

Colour the teddies who are asking "How are you?" in blue, and the ones who are saying "I'm fine, thank you" in pink.

Ça va bien, merci.   pink   pink

Ça va bien, merci.

pink

Ça va?   Ça va?

blue   blue

Jacques has asked Lily how she is. Complete Lily's speech bubble so that she says "not bad" in French.

Jacques

Ça va?

P a s   m a l .

Lily

6

## 7

Éric is all confused. Rewrite his answer below with the words in the correct order.

Ça va?

Éric

Antoine

Bien va merci ça.

Ça va bien merci.
...............................
...............................

Colour in the letters which spell out "ça va?".

**ç e a p a**
**k l v s ?**

Fill in the blanks to finish the conversation.

Ç a   v a ?

P a s   m a l .

7

## 8 What is your name?
### Comment t'appelles-tu?

To ask "What is your name?" in French, you say

**Comment t'appelles-tu?**

To say "My name is..." in French, you say

**Je m'appelle...**

Draw lines through the boxes to make two sentences.

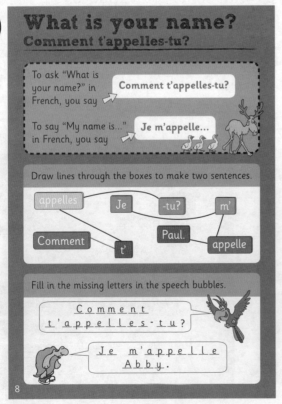

appelles   Je   -tu?   m'

Comment   Paul.   appelle

t'

Fill in the missing letters in the speech bubbles.

C o m m e n t
t ' a p p e l l e s - t u ?

J e   m ' a p p e l l e
A b b y .

8

Keep asking your child 'Comment t'appelles-tu?' so they can practise saying 'Je m'appelle...'.

## 9

Circle the correct French words to match the English.

| Hello | How are you? | My name is |
|---|---|---|
| Comment t'appelles-tu? | Je m'appelle | Au revoir |
| Ça va? | Au revoir | (Je m'appelle) |
| (Bonjour) | (Ça va?) | Comment t'appelles-tu? |

Gerald has sent you a secret message in French. Follow the instructions to find out what it says.

C a o m m t e b n u t
t ' a p p h e l u l e s - w t u ?

Cross out the blue boxes and write down what's left.
Comment t'appelles-tu?
...............................

Write down what this means in English.
What is your name?
...............................

9

# Numbers
## Les nombres

Here are the numbers from one to ten in French.

1 un  2 deux  3 trois  4 quatre  5 cinq  6 six  7 sept  8 huit  9 neuf  10 dix

Write the French word for each number below.

| 7 | sept | 1 | un |
|---|------|---|-----|
| 3 | trois | 4 | quatre |
| 8 | huit | 6 | six |

Draw lines to match the numbers to the French words.

10 quatre 5 neuf 2
cinq 9 deux 4 dix

10

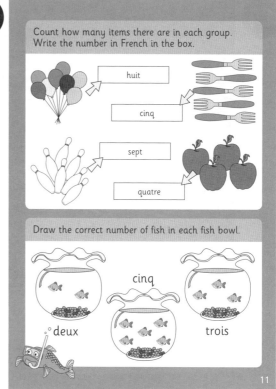

Count how many items there are in each group.
Write the number in French in the box.

huit

cinq

sept

quatre

Draw the correct number of fish in each fish bowl.

cinq

deux          trois

11

# Colours
## Les couleurs

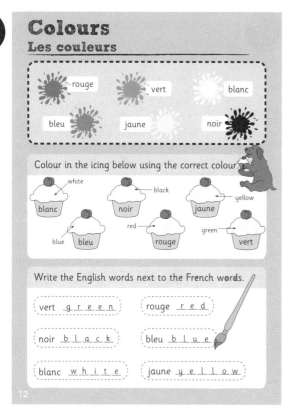

rouge    vert    blanc
bleu    jaune    noir

Colour in the icing below using the correct colour.

white — blanc
black — noir
yellow — jaune
blue — bleu
red — rouge
green — vert

Write the English words next to the French words.

vert g r e e n     rouge r e d
noir b l a c k     bleu b l u e
blanc w h i t e    jaune y e l l o w

12

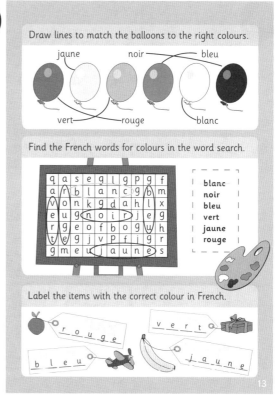

Draw lines to match the balloons to the right colours.

jaune    noir    bleu
vert    rouge    blanc

Find the French words for colours in the word search.

| q | a | s | e | g | l | g | p | g | f |
|---|---|---|---|---|---|---|---|---|---|
| a | r | b | l | a | n | c | g | b | m |
| v | o | n | k | g | d | a | h | l | x |
| e | u | g | n | o | i | r | j | e | g |
| r | g | e | o | f | b | o | g | u | h |
| t | e | g | j | v | p | f | j | g | r |
| g | m | e | u | j | a | u | n | e | s |

blanc
noir
bleu
vert
jaune
rouge

Label the items with the correct colour in French.

r o u g e          v e r t
b l e u            j a u n e

13

Encourage your child to point to items around the house and say what colour they are in French.

## 14 My family
### Ma famille

mon papa — my dad
ma maman — my mum
ma sœur — my sister
moi — me
mon frère — my brother
ma mamie — my granny
mon papi — my grandad

For each picture, colour in the family member that's mentioned.

**Remember!**
The word for "my" changes. If you are talking about a boy, use "**mon**", if you are talking about a girl use "**ma**".

You should have coloured in his mum.
Ma maman.
You should have coloured in his grandad.
Mon papi.

Make sure your child remembers to add accents to letters where needed, e.g. 'è' and that they are drawn in the right direction.

## 15

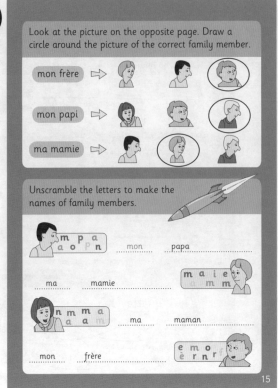

Look at the picture on the opposite page. Draw a circle around the picture of the correct family member.

mon frère ⇨
mon papi ⇨
ma mamie ⇨

Unscramble the letters to make the names of family members.

m p a a o P n → .......... mon .......... papa

m a i e a m m → .......... ma .......... mamie

n m m a a a m → .......... ma .......... maman

e m o è r n r → .......... mon .......... frère

For extra practice, you could ask your child to draw and label a picture of their family, or a family from their favourite TV programme, in French.

## 16 Animals
### Les animaux

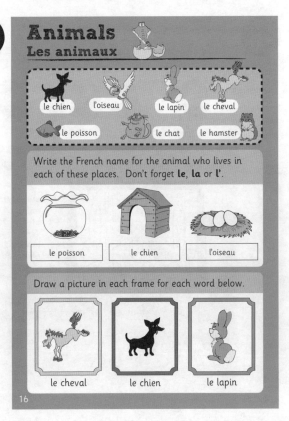

le chien    l'oiseau    le lapin    le cheval
le poisson    le chat    le hamster

Write the French name for the animal who lives in each of these places. Don't forget **le**, **la** or **l'**.

le poisson    le chien    l'oiseau

Draw a picture in each frame for each word below.

le cheval    le chien    le lapin

## 17

Colour each animal in the same colour as its word.

orange    l'oiseau    yellow
le lapin
blue    le chat    green    le poisson

Find your way through the maze. Write down the French names of the animals you meet on the way.

start

1. l'oiseau
2. le hamster
3. le poisson
4. le chien
5. le chat
6. le lapin
7. le cheval

finish

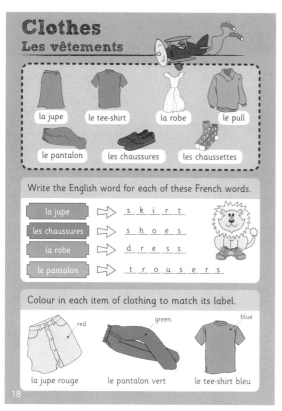

## Clothes
### Les vêtements

la jupe    le tee-shirt    la robe    le pull

le pantalon    les chaussures    les chaussettes

Write the English word for each of these French words.

la jupe ⟹ s k i r t

les chaussures ⟹ s h o e s

la robe ⟹ d r e s s

le pantalon ⟹ t r o u s e r s

Colour in each item of clothing to match its label.

red    green    blue

la jupe rouge    le pantalon vert    le tee-shirt bleu

As an extension exercise, you could ask your child to point out items of clothing, in French, in books or magazines.

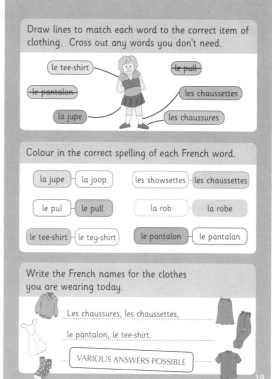

Draw lines to match each word to the correct item of clothing. Cross out any words you don't need.

le tee-shirt    le pull    le pantalon    les chaussettes    la jupe    les chaussures

Colour in the correct spelling of each French word.

la jupe   la joop    les showsettes   les chaussettes

le pul   le pull    la rob   la robe

le tee-shirt   le tey-shirt    le pantalon   le pantalan

Write the French names for the clothes you are wearing today.

Les chaussures, les chaussettes, le pantalon, le tee-shirt.

VARIOUS ANSWERS POSSIBLE

## What do you like doing?
### Qu'est-ce que tu aimes faire?

J'aime...    I like...

...jouer au foot   ...playing football

...regarder la télé   ...watching TV

...danser   ...dancing

...lire   ...reading

...nager   ...swimming

...écouter de la musique   ...listening to music

Colour in the pictures to match the correct sentences.

J'aime lire.   vert    blue

J'aime regarder la télé.   bleu

J'aime jouer au foot.   rouge    green    red

Complete the English sentence below about Gilles.

J'aime nager!   Gilles likes swimming

Gilles

Circle the pictures to show what Matthieu likes to do.

Bonjour! J'aime écouter de la musique, lire, jouer au foot et nager.

Matthieu

Follow the lines with a pencil to find out what each person likes to do. Match their name with the French.

Anna   J'aime danser.

Karine   J'aime écouter de la musique.

Tom   J'aime jouer au foot.

To extend this exercise, ask your child to write down in French what they like to do.

## 22

# Food
## La nourriture

la pomme

les frites

les spaghettis

le yaourt

le chocolat

le sandwich

le fromage

Unscramble these French words.

| s e i f  r l s t e | m e o  m a p l o | h c l a c  o l t o e |
|---|---|---|

les    frites        la    pomme        le    chocolat

Write the French word to match each picture.
The purple circles spell out a secret message.

l e f r o m a g e

l e c h o c o l a t

l e y a o u r t

l e s a n d w i c h

22

## 23

Draw pictures of food to match the labels.

les frites        le sandwich        les spaghettis

Circle the right picture for each word.

le yaourt ⇨

le fromage ⇨

les frites ⇨

Colour the pictures to match the correct words.

le sandwich

green

le yaourt

red

blue

les spaghettis

orange

la pomme

23

## 24

# In my pencil case
## Dans ma trousse

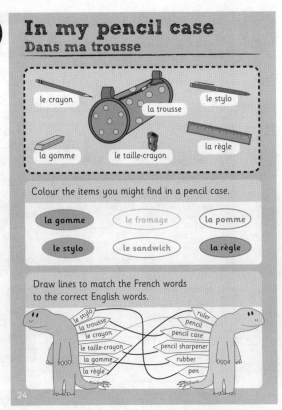

le crayon

la trousse

le stylo

la gomme

le taille-crayon

la règle

Colour the items you might find in a pencil case.

**la gomme**        le fromage        **la pomme**

**le stylo**        le sandwich        **la règle**

Draw lines to match the French words
to the correct English words.

le stylo
la trousse
le crayon
le taille-crayon
la gomme
la règle

ruler
pencil
pencil case
pencil sharpener
rubber
pen

24

To extend this exercise, your child could
write a list of the items they have in their
own pencil case, in French.

## 25

Write the French words for each of these pictures.

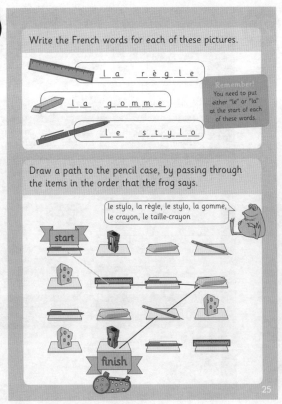

l a   r è g l e

l a   g o m m e

l e   s t y l o

**Remember!**
You need to put
either "le" or "la"
at the start of each
of these words.

Draw a path to the pencil case, by passing through
the items in the order that the frog says.

le stylo, la règle, le stylo, la gomme,
le crayon, le taille-crayon

start

finish

25

Encourage your child to remember to write
the article ('le' or 'la') when they are writing
French words.

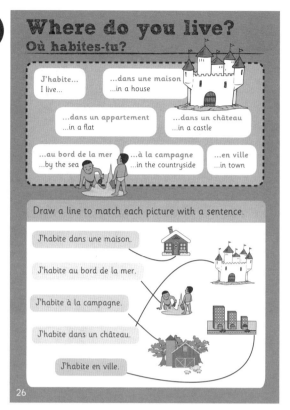

## 26 Where do you live?
### Où habites-tu?

J'habite...
I live...

...dans une maison
...in a house

...dans un appartement
...in a flat

...dans un château
...in a castle

...au bord de la mer
...by the sea

...à la campagne
...in the countryside

...en ville
...in town

Draw a line to match each picture with a sentence.

J'habite dans une maison.

J'habite au bord de la mer.

J'habite à la campagne.

J'habite dans un château.

J'habite en ville.

26

## 27

Read what each person is saying. Colour the correct picture to show where they live.

J'habite en ville.

J'habite à la campagne.

J'habite au bord de la mer.

Write where **you** live in French on the lines below and draw a picture to match.

J'habite...
dans une maison.
.... VARIOUS ANSWERS POSSIBLE

27

Some of the phrases on page 26 are quite tricky. Your child might like to read the teaching box again before trying each question.

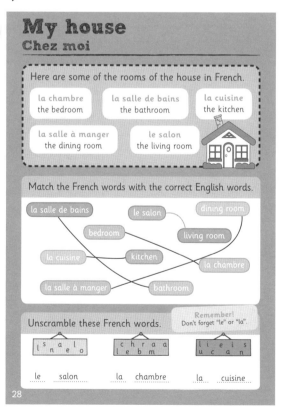

## 28 My house
### Chez moi

Here are some of the rooms of the house in French.

la chambre
the bedroom

la salle de bains
the bathroom

la cuisine
the kitchen

la salle à manger
the dining room

le salon
the living room

Match the French words with the correct English words.

la salle de bains

le salon

dining room

bedroom

living room

la cuisine

kitchen

la chambre

la salle à manger

bathroom

Unscramble these French words.

**Remember!**
Don't forget "le" or "la".

s a l
l n e o

c h r a a
l e b m

l i e i s
u c a n

le    salon

la    chambre

la    cuisine

28

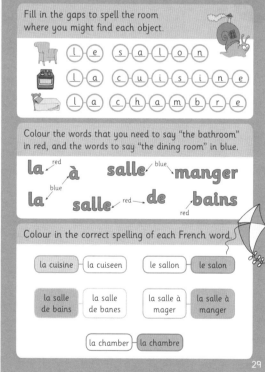

## 29

Fill in the gaps to spell the room where you might find each object.

l e   s a l o n

l a   c u i s i n e

l a   c h a m b r e

Colour the words that you need to say "the bathroom" in red, and the words to say "the dining room" in blue.

la (red)   à   salle (blue)   manger
(blue)
la   salle (red)   de   bains (red)

Colour in the correct spelling of each French word.

la cuisine    la cuiseen    le sallon    le salon

la salle de bains    la salle de banes    la salle à mager    la salle à manger

la chamber    la chambre

29

For extra practice, ask your child to draw a plan of where they live, and to label it in French.

# Do you remember?
## Tu te rappelles?

What is your name? **Comment t'appelles-tu?**
Write a reply, in French, in the gaps below.

Je m'appelle

Lucy    VARIOUS ANSWERS POSSIBLE

Colour the splats of paint in the right colours.

bleu — blue
blanc — white
rouge — red
vert — green
noir — black
jaune — yellow

Circle the correct French words to match the English.

| the rabbit | the kitchen | goodbye |
|---|---|---|
| le fromage | la pomme | (au revoir) |
| le pull | le salon | je m'appelle |
| (le lapin) | le stylo | Comment t'appelles-tu? |
| la trousse | (la cuisine) | |

30

---

Colour in the words for the clothes you are wearing.

le pantalon    le tee-shirt
les chaussettes
le pull    la [VARIOUS ANSWERS POSSIBLE]
les chaussures    la jupe

Circle the three foods that Michael is eating.

le chocolat    le fromage    les frites
la pomme    le yaourt

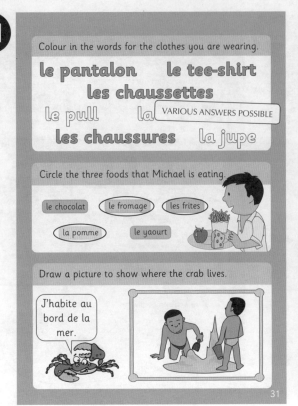

Draw a picture to show where the crab lives.

J'habite au bord de la mer.

31

---

Pages 30 and 31 test a variety of subjects from throughout the book. If your child finds any of them tricky, encourage them to look back through the book to find the answer.

---

## Race to the top of the Eiffel Tower

You'll need a counter for each player and a dice. Place your counters on the first square, and take it in turns to roll the dice once. Follow the instructions when you land on them.

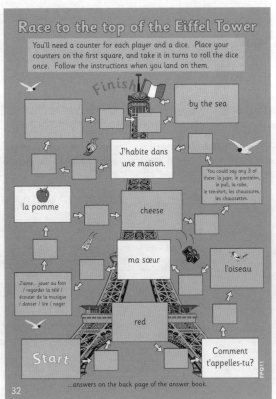

Finish

by the sea

J'habite dans une maison.

You could say any 3 of these: la jupe, le pantalon, le pull, la robe, le tee-shirt, les chaussures, les chaussettes.

la pomme

cheese

ma sœur

l'oiseau

J'aime... jouer au foot / regarder la télé / écouter de la musique / danser / lire / nager.

red

Start

Comment t'appelles-tu?

FP011

...answers on the back page of the answer book.

32

## Colour each animal in the same colour as its word.

l'oiseau

le lapin

le chat

le poisson

## Find your way through the maze. Write down the French names of the animals you meet on the way.

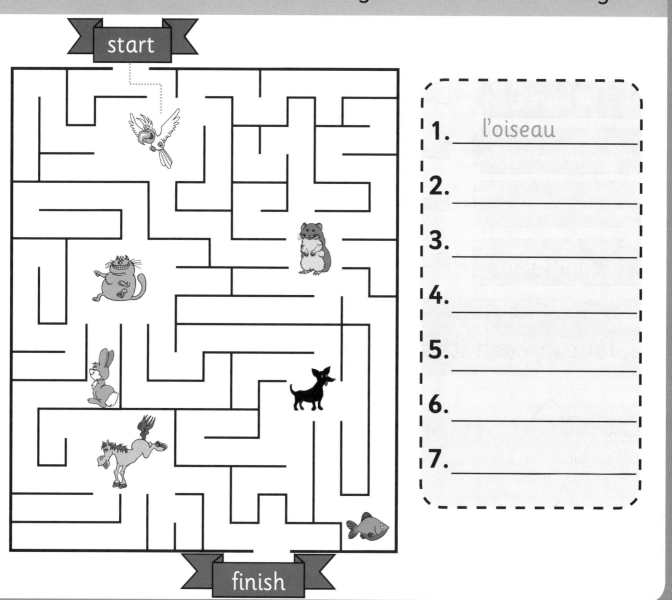

start

1. _l'oiseau_

2. _____

3. _____

4. _____

5. _____

6. _____

7. _____

finish

17

# Clothes
## Les vêtements

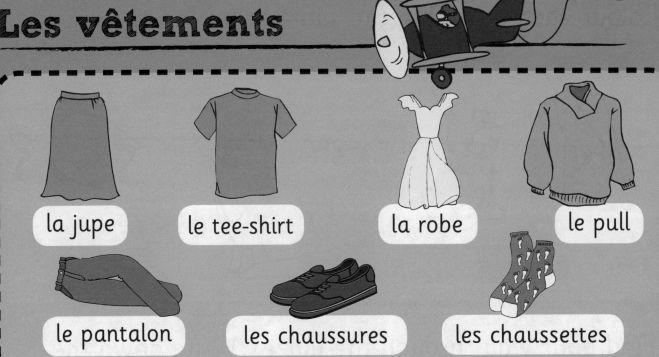

la jupe    le tee-shirt    la robe    le pull

le pantalon    les chaussures    les chaussettes

Write the English word for each of these French words.

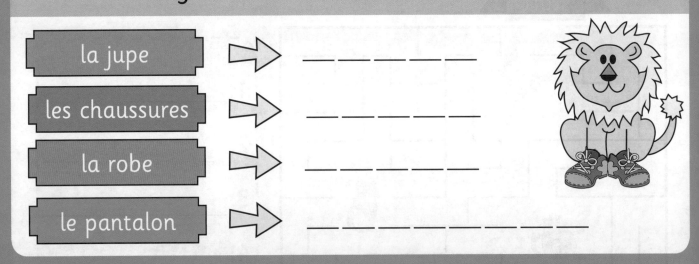

la jupe ➡ _ _ _ _ _

les chaussures ➡ _ _ _ _ _

la robe ➡ _ _ _ _ _

le pantalon ➡ _ _ _ _ _ _ _

Colour in each item of clothing to match its label.

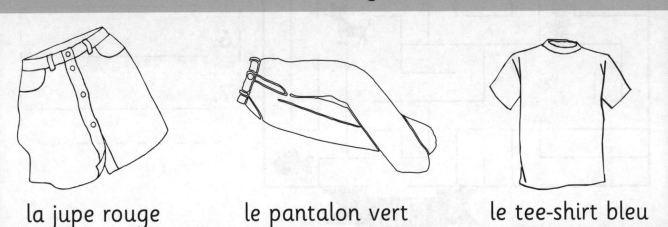

la jupe rouge    le pantalon vert    le tee-shirt bleu

Draw lines to match each word to the correct item of clothing. Cross out any words you don't need.

le tee-shirt

le pantalon

la jupe

le pull

les chaussettes

les chaussures

Colour in the correct spelling of each French word.

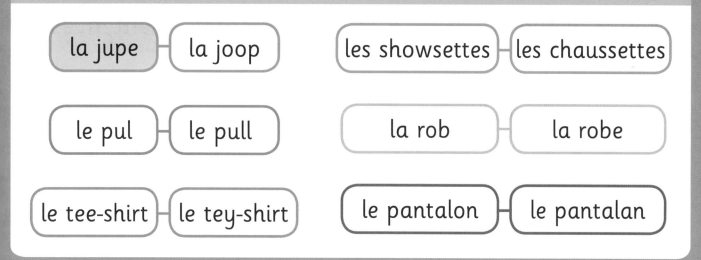

la jupe — la joop

les showsettes — les chaussettes

le pul — le pull

la rob — la robe

le tee-shirt — le tey-shirt

le pantalon — le pantalan

Write the French names for the clothes you are wearing today.

..................................................................................................

..................................................................................................

..................................................................................................

19

# What do you like doing?
## Qu'est-ce que tu aimes faire?

**J'aime...**     I like...

**...jouer au foot**
...playing football

**...regarder la télé**
...watching TV

**...danser**
...dancing

**...lire**
...reading

**...nager**
...swimming

**...écouter de la musique**
...listening to music

---

Colour in the pictures to match the correct sentences.

J'aime lire.

 J'aime regarder la télé.

J'aime jouer au foot.

---

Complete the English sentence below about Gilles.

J'aime nager!

Gilles

Gilles likes

...............................................

20

Circle the pictures to show what Matthieu likes to do.

Follow the lines with a pencil to find out what each person likes to do. Match their name with the French.

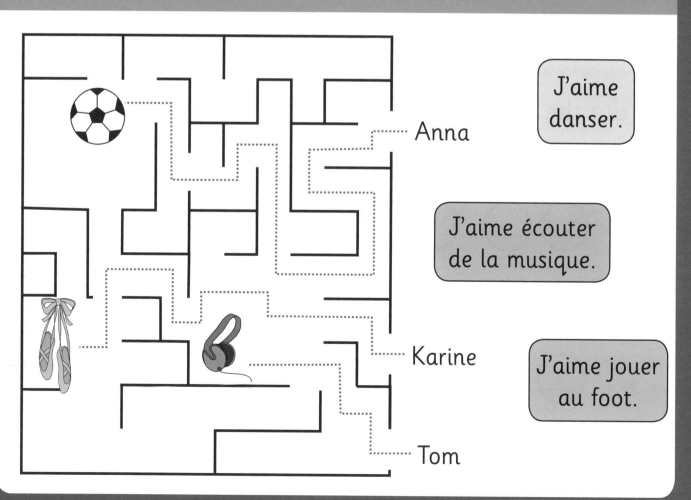

# Food
# La nourriture

la pomme

les frites

les spaghettis

le yaourt

le chocolat

le sandwich

le fromage

Unscramble these French words.

................  ..............        ........  ...............        ........  ...............

Write the French word to match each picture.
The purple circles spell out a secret message.

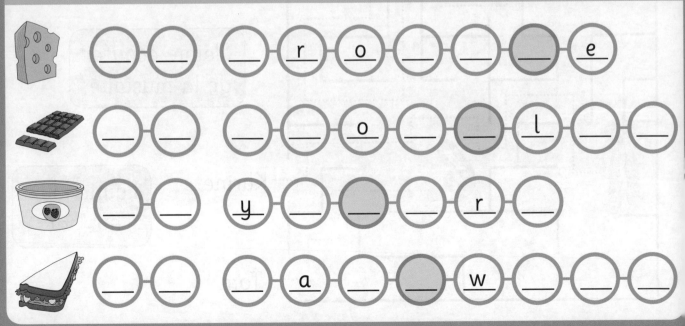

22

## Draw pictures of food to match the labels.

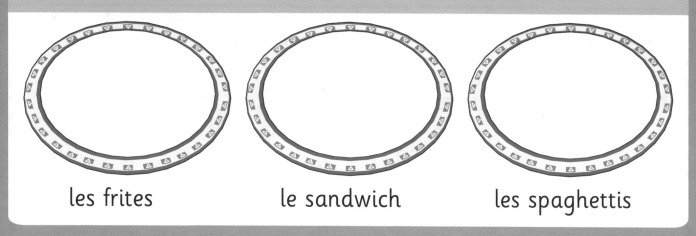

les frites      le sandwich      les spaghettis

## Circle the right picture for each word.

le yaourt ⇨

le fromage ⇨

les frites ⇨

## Colour the pictures to match the correct words.

le sandwich

le yaourt

les spaghettis

la pomme

# In my pencil case
## Dans ma trousse

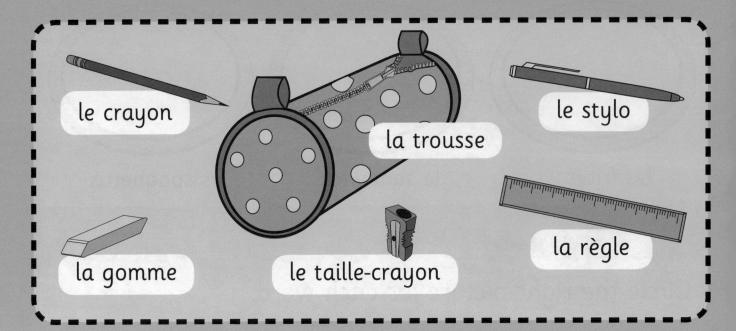

le crayon

la trousse

le stylo

la règle

la gomme

le taille-crayon

Colour the items you might find in a pencil case.

la gomme

le fromage

la pomme

le stylo

le sandwich

la règle

Draw lines to match the French words
to the correct English words.

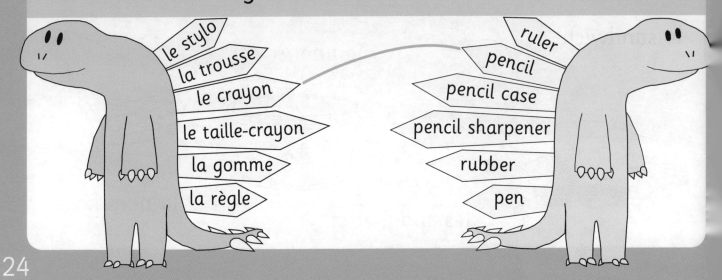

le stylo

la trousse

le crayon

le taille-crayon

la gomme

la règle

ruler

pencil

pencil case

pencil sharpener

rubber

pen

# Write the French words for each of these pictures.

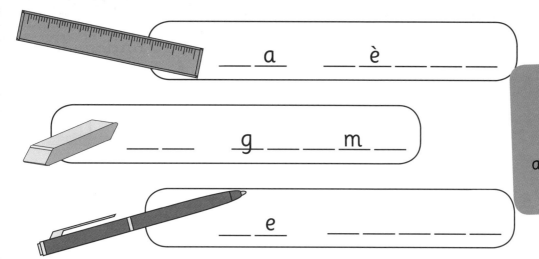

__ __ a __ __ __ è __ __ __

__ __ __ g __ __ m __ __

__ __ e __ __ __ __ __ __ __

**Remember!**
You need to put either "le" or "la" at the start of each of these words.

# Draw a path to the pencil case, by passing through the items in the order that the frog says.

le stylo, la règle, le stylo, la gomme, le crayon, le taille-crayon

# Where do you live?
## Où habites-tu?

J'habite...
I live...

...dans une maison
...in a house

...dans un appartement
...in a flat

...dans un château
...in a castle

...au bord de la mer
...by the sea

...à la campagne
...in the countryside

...en ville
...in town

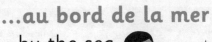

Draw a line to match each picture with a sentence.

J'habite dans une maison.

J'habite au bord de la mer.

J'habite à la campagne.

J'habite dans un château.

J'habite en ville.

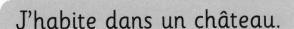

Read what each person is saying. Colour the correct picture to show where they live.

Write where **you** live in French on the lines below and draw a picture to match.

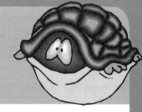

J'habite...

.....................................

.....................................

.....................................

# My house
## Chez moi

Here are some of the rooms of the house in French.

**la chambre**
the bedroom

**la salle de bains**
the bathroom

**la cuisine**
the kitchen

**la salle à manger**
the dining room

**le salon**
the living room

Match the French words with the correct English words.

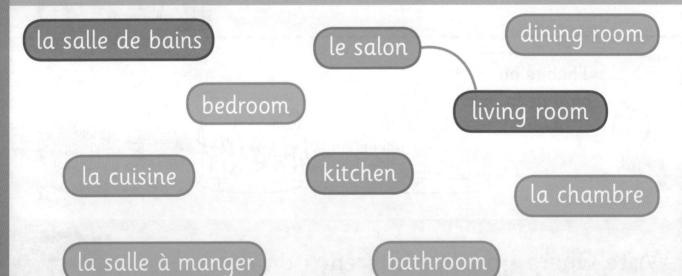

la salle de bains

le salon

dining room

bedroom

living room

la cuisine

kitchen

la chambre

la salle à manger

bathroom

Unscramble these French words.

**Remember!**
Don't forget "le" or "la".

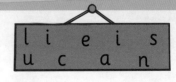

l s a l
n e o

c h r a a
l e b m

l i e i s
u c a n

........ ................

........ ................

........ ................

Fill in the gaps to spell the room where you might find each object.

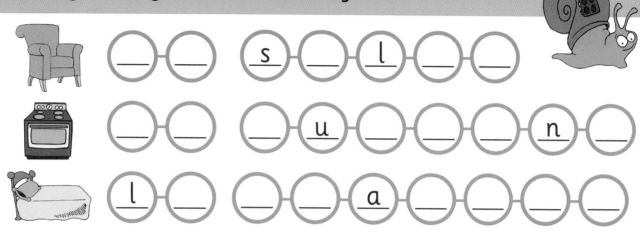

Colour the words that you need to say "the bathroom" in red, and the words to say "the dining room" in blue.

la    à    salle    manger

la    salle    de    bains

Colour in the correct spelling of each French word.

| la cuisine | la cuiseen | | le sallon | le salon |

| la salle de bains | la salle de banes | | la salle à mager | la salle à manger |

la chamber — la chambre

# Do you remember?
## Tu te rappelles?

What is your name? **Comment t'appelles-tu?**
Write a reply, in French, in the gaps below.

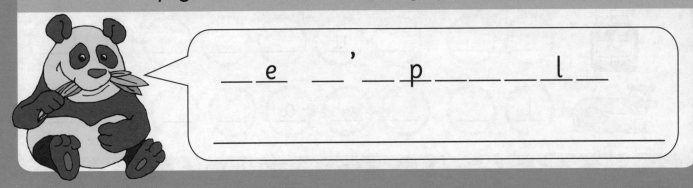

_ _ e _ _ ' _ p _ _ _ _ l _

Colour the splats of paint in the right colours.

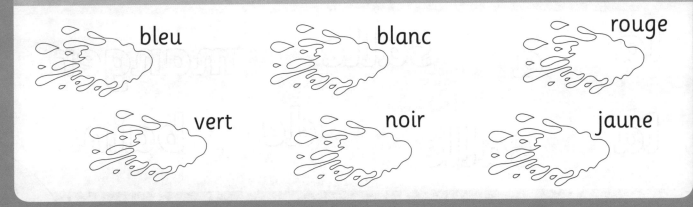

bleu

blanc

rouge

vert

noir

jaune

Circle the correct French words to match the English.

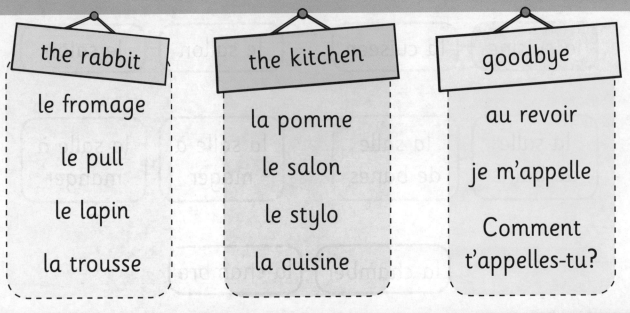

| the rabbit | the kitchen | goodbye |
|---|---|---|
| le fromage | la pomme | au revoir |
| le pull | le salon | je m'appelle |
| le lapin | le stylo | Comment t'appelles-tu? |
| la trousse | la cuisine | |

Colour in the words for the clothes you are wearing.

# le pantalon    le tee-shirt
# les chaussettes
# le pull    la robe
# les chaussures    la jupe

Circle the three foods that Michael is eating.

le chocolat    le fromage    les frites

la pomme    le yaourt

Draw a picture to show where the crab lives.

J'habite au bord de la mer.

# Race to the top of the Eiffel Tower

You'll need a counter for each player and a dice. Place your counters on the first square, and take it in turns to roll the dice once. Follow the instructions when you land on them.

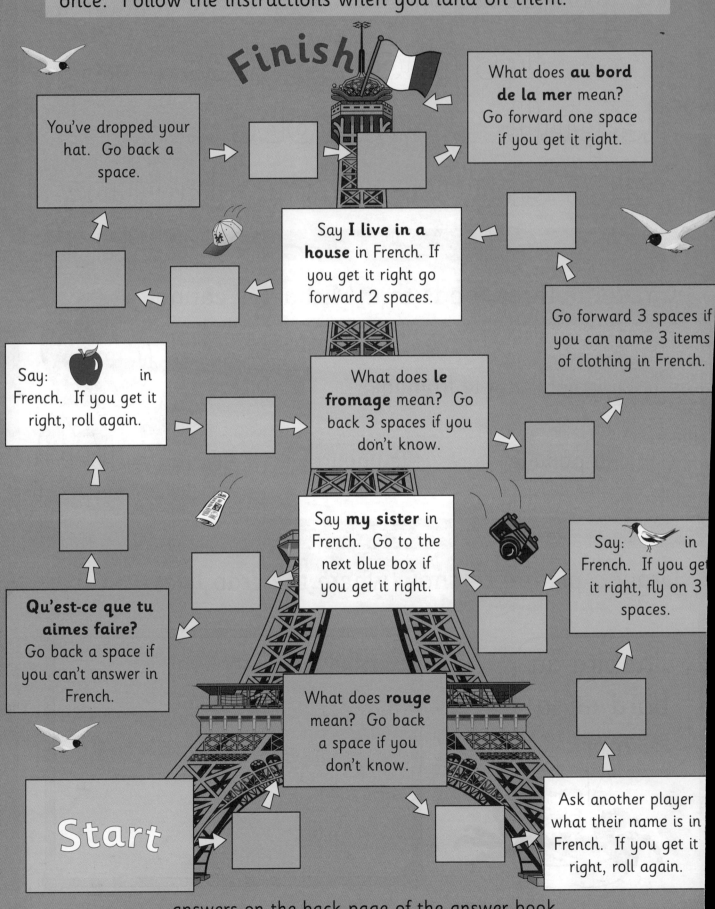

Finish

You've dropped your hat. Go back a space.

What does **au bord de la mer** mean? Go forward one space if you get it right.

Say **I live in a house** in French. If you get it right go forward 2 spaces.

Go forward 3 spaces if you can name 3 items of clothing in French.

Say: 🍎 in French. If you get it right, roll again.

What does **le fromage** mean? Go back 3 spaces if you don't know.

Say **my sister** in French. Go to the next blue box if you get it right.

Say: 🐦 in French. If you get it right, fly on 3 spaces.

**Qu'est-ce que tu aimes faire?** Go back a space if you can't answer in French.

What does **rouge** mean? Go back a space if you don't know.

Ask another player what their name is in French. If you get it right, roll again.

Start

...answers on the back page of the answer book.